MW00623028

THE SAILING SAINT

ISBN# 1-930710-37-2

Veritas Press, Lancaster, Pennsylvania
800-922-5082
www.VeritasPress.com

First edition

THE SAILING SAINT

written·and·illustrated·by·ned·bustard

Veritas Press

this book
is dedicated
to my dad—
for passing on
to me irish blood,
faith in god,
and a love
of sailing.

Saint Brendan was a monk long ago.
Brendan did love to pray and sail.

Brendan told all he met of Christ.
Some told Brendan of a blest land
that lies past the sunset.

Brendan began praying to ask God to go
to find that land. Then one May day
they began the quest.

Brendan and some monks put tan skins
over thin branches to make a boat.
Brendan made oars and a sail for the boat.

The monks laid dried fish, grain, and
sea moss in the boat for meals.

"God the One Person of the Three,
Bless the boat" said Brendan.

In the fall Saint Brendan and his monks set
sail into the deep sea. "May the hand of
God pilot us" said Brendan.

The boat went floating along the coast.
The wind sent the ship north.

They saw a wee land full of sheep.
They saw a wee land full of birds.

A big rain came, pushing the boat hard
for weeks. Their meals dried up.
The monks were full of dread.

The storm sent them spinning into a cove.
In the cove were monks like Brendan.

With cheer they all did take part in
the Christ Mass. Then they ate a
feast of roast boar and pies.

On the next gay day, Brendan and
the monks went on their way.

Then they came to a cold sea. It was full
of floating white hills of great size.

Brendan set their boat on the quay of
one of the frosty blocks. The monks
had church there before going on.

Sailing into the sunset, the monks came to
a land that had hills that spat hot rocks.
Brendan and the monks fled the fray.

Then at Easter the boat came to rest
on a wee land. Brendan gave the
monks the Bread and the Wine.
Then a monk tried to make a fire.

The land rose and dove. The land was
a whale! The monks got in the boat.

Wake from the whale broke across the
boat, soaking all their cloaks. They all
had to bail and bail with pails.

Weeks and weeks later Brendan
spied a lush land. It was warm
and pretty with singing birds.

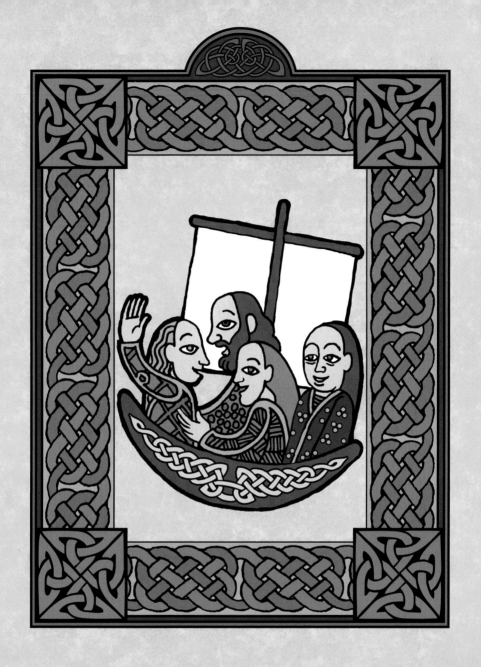

All the monks sang praises to God, thanking
Him for bringing them there. Brendan gave
the land the name "Hy Brasil."

Brendan met a tribe of tan lads and lasses.
Brendan told them of Christ.

Then Brendan and his team of monks
went across the land and back.

Brendan began longing for their green
home. The monks put water, pineapples
and breads in the boat.

"May Christ be with us. Christ before us.
Christ in us. Christ over us," Brendan said
to God as the little band of monks
set sail for home.